This book is a special gift for YOU!

Fiona Ryan

To inspire a lifetime of word collecting and
celebrating for you and your family!

Enjoy every word!

A national pilot initiative led by

Children's
Reading
Connection

www.childrensreadingconnection.org

the Word Collector

dedicated to Dick Robinson,
who has inspired word collectors worldwide.

—P.H.R.

ISBN 978-1-338-33157-8

12 11 10 9 8 7 6 5 4 3 2   18 19 20 21 22 23

Printed in the U.S.A.   40

This edition first printing, September 2018

The text type and display are hand-lettered by Peter H. Reynolds.
Reynolds Studio assistance by Julia Anne Young • Book design by Patti Ann Harris

the Word Collector

PETER HAMILTON REYNOLDS

Scholastic Inc.

Collectors collect things...

Some people collect stamps.

Some people collect coins.

Others collect rocks.

Some collect art.

Some collect bugs.

Others collect baseball cards.

Some people collect comic books.

And Jerome? What did HE collect?

Jerome collected words.

He collected words he **heard.**

Certain words caught his attention.

He collected words he **saw.**

WILLOW

WILLOW
TEA SHOPPE

Certain words jumped out at him.

He collected words he
read.

Certain words popped off the page.

Short and sweet words.

Two-syllable treats.

And multi-syllable words that
sounded like little songs.

There were words he did not know the
meaning of at first, but they were

marvelous

to say.

There were words whose sounds were perfectly suited to their meaning.

Jerome filled his scrapbooks with
more and more
of his favorite words.

Jerome's collections grew. He began organizing them.
"DREAMY" "SCIENCE" "SAD" "ACTION" "POETIC"
One day, while transporting them—

Jerome slipped and
his words went
flying!

As he began to pick them up, he noticed
his collections had become
jumbled.

Big words next to little words.
Sad words next to dreamy words.

Words he had not imagined being
side by side.

He used his words
to write poems.

He used his poems to make songs.

They moved. They delighted.

Some of his simplest words were his most

powerful.

Jerome eagerly collected
more and more
of his favorite words.

The more words he knew the more
clearly he could share with the world
what he was thinking, feeling, and dreaming.

One breezy afternoon,
Jerome climbed the highest hill,
pulling a wagon packed with
his word collection.

He smiled as he
emptied his collection of words
into the wind.

He saw children in the valley below…

...scurrying about collecting words from the breeze.

Jerome
had no words
to describe how happy
that made him.

REACH FOR YOUR OWN WORDS

TELL THE WORLD WHO YOU ARE

AND HOW YOU WILL MAKE IT BETTER

—PETER HAMILTON REYNOLDS

Peter H. Reynolds is a *New York Times* bestselling author and illustrator of many books for children, including *The Dot*, *Ish*, and *Happy Dreamer*. His books have been translated into over twenty-five languages around the globe and are celebrated worldwide. In 1996, he founded FableVision with his brother, Paul, as a social change agency to help create "stories that matter, stories that move." He lives in Dedham, Massachusetts, with his family. www.peterhreynolds.com